STORYTELLING GUIDANCE

Five Reproducible Interactive Stories With Activities
For Young Children

WRITTEN BY
Melinda Saenz Villegas

ILLUSTRATED BY
Terry Sirrell

DEDICATION

This book is dedicated to my little miracle, Nicholas Andrew Villegas, who was in my womb at the time I wrote this book. Thank you for keeping me sleepless at night, allowing me plenty of time to write these stories.

STORYTELLING GUIDANCE

10-DIGIT ISBN: 1-57543-126-2   13-DIGIT ISBN: 978-1-57543-126-0

REPRINTED 2006
COPYRIGHT © 2004 MAR*CO PRODUCTS, INC.
Published by mar∗co products, inc.
1443 Old York Road
Warminster, PA 18974
1-800-448-2197
www.marcoproducts.com

PRINTED IN THE U.S.A.

CONTENTS

STORYTELLING GUIDANCE

(Introduction)

The five stories included in this program emphasize character traits and behaviors which, if instilled in children at an early age, will enhance any child's educational experience.

Young children love to have their own storybooks, and these stories are intended for reproduction. They are written in a format that allows each child to understand the intent of the materials including comprehension and self-insight questions and activities throughout each story. By completing the activities or questions and coloring the pictures, each child creates a personal book to read over and over again and share with his/her parents.

Each story also includes one or more follow-up activities. Use these activities to conclude each lesson.

If reproducing the stories for each child is not appropriate, read the stories aloud to the children. In this case, you may wish to reproduce a copy, bind it, and color the pictures before making the presentation. When making a presentation of this kind, stop and elicit answers to the material presented throughout the story.

THE PROUD PEPPERONI

(Respecting Differences)

OBJECTIVE:

Children will learn that it is important to understand and accept differences and give others a chance before forming opinions about them. Children will also learn to get along better with others.

MATERIALS NEEDED:

For each child:
- ☐ Copy of *The Proud Pepperoni* (pages 8-11)
- ☐ Copy of *Multicultural Pizza* (pages 12-13)
- ☐ Copy of *Circle Of Friends* (pages 14-15)
- ☐ Copy of *Take The Pizza To The Oven Maze* (page 16)
- ☐ Copy of *Notes For Accepting Others* (page 17)
- ☐ Pencil
- ☐ Crayons or markers
- ☐ Scissors
- ☐ Paste or glue stick

For the leader:
- ☐ Chalkboard and chalk
- ☐ Stapler and staples

PRE-PRESENTATION PREPARATION:

Reproduce the necessary materials for the children. Staple the story pages into a booklet for each child. Read the story. Be prepared to review any unfamiliar or difficult-to-read words with the children prior to distributing the booklets.

STORYTELLING GUIDANCE © 2004 MAR✱CO PRODUCTS, INC. 1-800-448-2197

INTRODUCING THE LESSON:

Ask the children:

What is your favorite topping on pizza? *(Pause for responses. You may want to graph responses on the chalkboard to see which topping the children prefer.)*

Today we are going to read a story about one topping that thinks it is the best. It thinks that it is better than all the rest! Can you guess which one of these toppings thinks it is the best? *(Allow several children to answer the question.)*

Introduce any unfamiliar or difficult-to-read words used in the story.

If the children are reading the story themselves or as a group, distribute *The Proud Pepperoni* and a pencil to each child. Have the children take turns reading the story aloud. After reading each page and before going on to the next, have the children complete the activities on the page that's been read. You may briefly discuss their answers.

After reading the story, give each child *Multicultural Pizza, Circle Of Friends, Take The Pizza To The Oven Maze,* crayons or markers, scissors, and paste or a glue stick. Have the children complete *Multicultural Pizza* and *Circle Of Friends*. Allow children who finish before the allotted time is up to color the pictures in their storybooks and complete the *Take The Pizza To The Oven Maze.*

Discuss the meaning of the *Multicultural Pizza* and *Circle Of Friends* activity sheets.

Give each child *Notes For Accepting Others*. Review its suggestions with the children.

Thank the children for their cooperation. Tell them they may take their storybooks, activity sheets, and posters home. Encourage the children to read their storybooks with their parents.

STORYTELLING GUIDANCE © 2004 MAR✳CO PRODUCTS, INC. 1-800-448-2197

THE PROUD PEPPERONI

I am a little pepperoni and
I think I am the best.
When you eat me on a pizza,
I'm better than all the rest.

My bright red coat's so tasty
with spices mixed so fine,
that people always want me
on their pizza all the time.

Pepperoni pizza is the kind
that makes the biggest hit.
So don't mix me with the others,
'cause I'll yell and throw a fit!

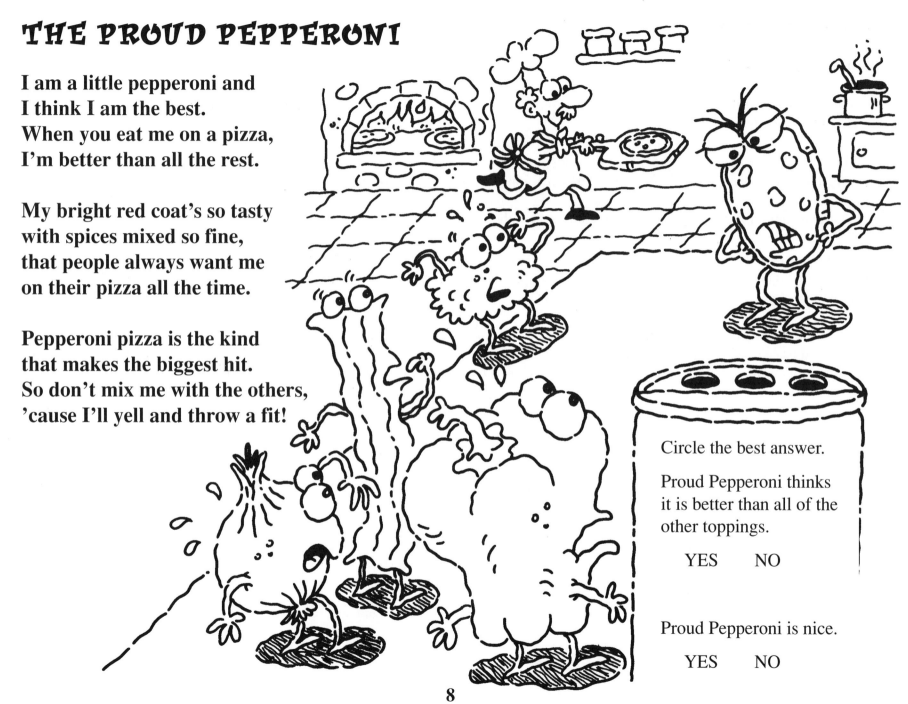

Circle the best answer.

Proud Pepperoni thinks
it is better than all of the
other toppings.

YES   NO

Proud Pepperoni is nice.

YES   NO

8

The bell pepper and the onion
taste so bitter you can cry.
The sausage and the bacon
taste so yucky. I can't lie.

So don't mix me with the others.
I only like my kind.
The others are so different.
I want them left behind.

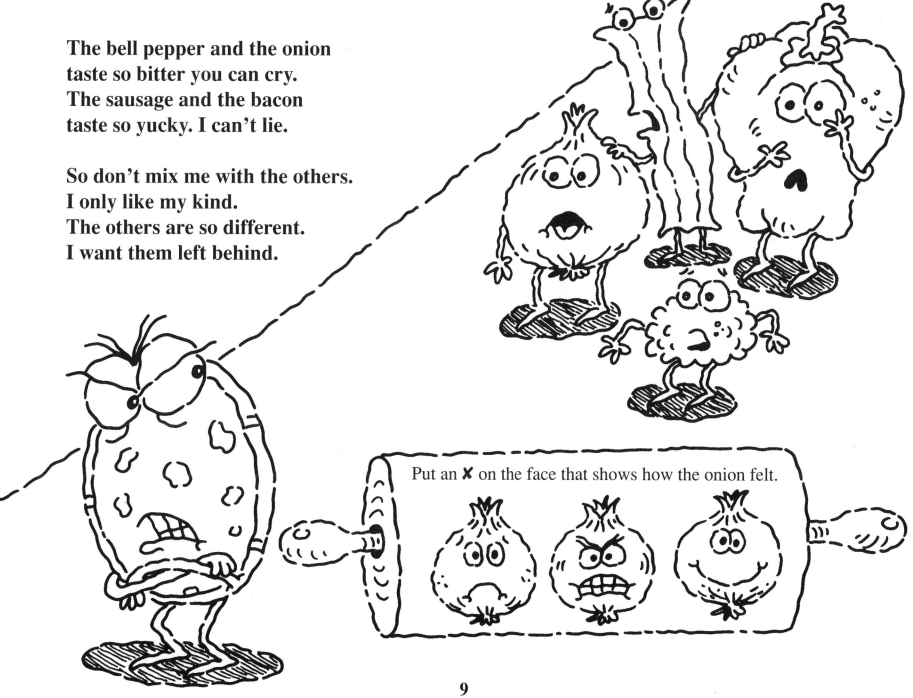

Put an ✗ on the face that shows how the onion felt.

9

"Sorry," says the cook,
"but differences make us great.
If you open up your heart
you'll see others are first-rate."

The cook placed the pepperoni
all neatly in a row.
Then tossed in all the others
really, really slow.

The pepperoni yelled,
"Don't mix me with the others.
I only like my kind.
The others are so different.
I want them left behind."

Look at each picture and write the letter above it on the blank. Then you will know what the cook told Proud Pepperoni.

_ p _ n up

y _ u _

h _ _ _ _ .

= a
= e
= o
= r
= t

The oven was so hot
as the pizza went inside.
The pepperoni couldn't get away;
there was nowhere to hide.

So it cooked with all the others
and the aroma was so great.
Proud Pepperoni had no choice
so he had this to state:

"Each one of us is special
in our very own unique way.
But together we're a great combination
and that's the way we'll stay."

STORYTELLING GUIDANCE © 2004 MAR✳CO PRODUCTS, INC. 1-800-448-2197

MULTICULTURAL PIZZA

Use the ingredients on the following page to make your own special pizza.

Color the ingredients. Then cut out the ones you want and paste them on your pizza.

| PEPPERONI | MUSHROOMS | ONIONS | GREEN PEPPERS | SAUSAGE. |

14

Cut out the faces that are like
the friends you have or are like
friends you would like to have
and paste them in your
Circle Of Friends.

TAKE THE PIZZA TO THE OVEN MAZE

Follow the path through the maze to the center of the pizza.
When you reach the center, color the pizza toppings.

START

NOTES FOR ACCEPTING OTHERS

1

Remember that we are all different.

2

Differences make us special.

3

Don't judge others by the way they look on the outside.

4

Get to know others on the inside.

STORYTELLING GUIDANCE © 2004 MAR✳CO PRODUCTS, INC. 1-800-448-2197

THE ANGRY VEGETABLES

(Handling Anger)

OBJECTIVE:

Children will learn that fighting doesn't solve anything and learn appropriate ways to release anger.

MATERIALS NEEDED:

For each child:
- ☐ Copy of *The Angry Vegetables* (pages 20-27)
- ☐ Copy of *The Vegetable Cooldown* (optional—page 28)
- ☐ Pencil
- ☐ Crayons or markers

For the leader:
- ☐ Stapler and staples
- ☐ Scissors
- ☐ Copy of *The Vegetable Cooldown* (page 28)
- ☐ CD or cassette player with CD or cassette of instrumental music
- ☐ Several pillows
- ☐ Several stuffed animals
- ☐ Copy of *The Vegetable Talk Role-Play Situation Cards* (page 29)

PRE-PRESENTATION PREPARATION:

Reproduce the necessary materials for the children. Staple the story pages together into a booklet for each child. Read the story. Be prepared to review any unfamiliar or difficult-to-read words with the children prior to distributing the booklets. Reproduce a copy of *The Vegetable Talk Role-Play Situation Cards* and cut them apart.

STORYTELLING GUIDANCE © 2004 MAR✳CO PRODUCTS, INC. 1-800-448-2197

INTRODUCING THE LESSON:

Begin the lesson by saying:

> We all get angry at one time or another. Anger is a normal emotion. It's okay to get angry. But when we get angry, we need to be careful about what we do with our anger. Some people handle their anger in an appropriate manner. Others do not. When we choose to handle our anger by hitting others, yelling at others, destroying property, or in some other inappropriate way, then we are not solving anything. We are making the problem worse.
>
> Today we are going to read *The Angry Vegetables*. In the story, the vegetables become angry with each other and get into a fight. Their problems can't be settled by fighting, so a trusted friend steps in and helps the vegetables participate in an activity that will release their anger energy in a safe way. After reading the story, we will learn some ways to handle our anger when we become upset.

Introduce any unfamiliar or difficult-to-read words used in the story.

If the children are reading the story themselves or as a group, distribute *The Angry Vegetables,* crayons or markers, and a pencil to each child. Have the children take turns reading the story aloud. After reading each page and before going on to the next, have the children complete the activities on the page that's been read. You may briefly discuss their answers.

After reading the story, use *The Vegetable Cooldown,* instrumental music, pillows, and stuffed animals to teach the children anger-management techniques. Demonstrate each technique. *The Vegetable Jive:* Play music and have the children move their bodies. *The Vegetable Hug:* Have several children practice hugging the stuffed animals. *The Vegetable Punch:* Have several children practice hitting the pillow. *The Vegetable Throw:* Have several children make a tight fist and throw away their angry feelings. After completing the activity, you may give the children a copy of *The Vegetable Cooldown* as a reminder of the anger-management techniques they have just learned.

Divide the children into pairs. Then say:

> Each pair of children will receive a card that describes a situation. Each of the situations would make a person angry. You are to think about the situation and decide which of the anger-management techniques you have just learned would be best to use. Then, when it is your turn, you are to act out the solution you have chosen.

Distribute a *The Vegetable Talk Role-Play Situation Card* to each pair of children and tell them how much time they have to complete the activity. When the allotted time has elapsed, have each pair of children read the situation from the card and enact its solution.

If time allows, have the children color the illustrations in their booklets. If there is not enough time, tell them to finish them at home.

Thank the children for their cooperation. Tell them they may take their storybooks and posters home.

THE ANGRY VEGETABLES

Circle the vegetables you like:

CARROT   BROCCOLI   PEAS   BEANS

SPINACH   POTATO   SQUASH

BRUSSELS   CELERY   PEPPER
SPROUTS

Once upon a time, there was a house.
In this house there stood a tall, stout refrigerator.

And in this refrigerator there lived a
healthy bunch of raw vegetables.

These vegetables were a great bunch.
And, boy, did they have fun in that refrigerator!

When the broccoli told a joke,
the carrot and celery laughed so hard
they lost their crispness for a while.

A person I know who tells funny jokes is

_____

21

These vegetables usually got along with each other.
But there was a time when things did not go very well.

It happened one day when the vegetables decided
to play a game in their wide, roomy refrigerator.

Draw a line to the face that shows how
you feel when playing a game if:

a. someone cheats.

b. everyone takes a turn.

c. everyone follows the rules.

d. someone gets angry.

e. someone hits another player.

f. someone does not play fairly.

Fill in the missing letters:

Broccoli Bunch was

A ＿＿＿ G ＿＿＿＿＿＿

Everything was going well until Broccoli Bunch
felt Bobby Bell Pepper push him really hard.

Broccoli Bunch got so angry,
he hit Bobby Bell Pepper really hard on the head.

When Carmela Carrot saw what was going on,
she joined in the fight.

"Stop it!" yelled Leafy Lettuce.
"Fighting is no good.
You know it doesn't solve anything."

"If you are angry," she said,
"let your anger out in a safe way."

Find and circle the letters that tell who
tried to stop the fight.

A B N O I C A R R O T R E
P E P P E R F H B X S Q R
M L E A F Y L E T T U C E
B R O C C O L I N V F L E
L E A C G R M E L A B V X
B E K L M V C X D T T U C

The vegetables followed Leafy Lettuce to the stove. Leafy Lettuce started boiling a pot of water.

Carmela Carrot was the first to jump in. Broccoli Bunch and Bobby Bell Pepper quickly followed.

"Ahh, Ahh, Ahh!" they all screamed.
They jumped up and down until they
felt their anger flow out of their bodies.

Circle the best answer.

Do you think what Leafy Lettuce is
doing will help stop the fighting?

YES   NO

"I feel great," said Bobby Bell Pepper.
"I'm ready to play fair."

Carmela was next. "I feel exhausted," she said.
"I am ready for a nap."

Put an ✗ on the faces that show how the vegetables felt.

STORYTELLING GUIDANCE © 2004 MAR✳CO PRODUCTS, INC. 1-800-448-2197

Broccoli Bunch spent a little more time in the pot. He wondered why he got so angry when Bobby Bell Pepper pushed him. "I should not have pushed him back," he thought. "I should have asked him to stop. I should have told him how his actions made me feel."

Just then, Leafy Lettuce came over and helped Broccoli Bunch out of the pot. "We better go back to the fridge," she said. "The lady of the house is home!"

Circle the pictures that show what Broccoli Bunch should have done instead of pushing Bobby Bell Pepper.

THE VEGETABLE COOLDOWN

When you feel angry, you suddenly have a lot of energy. We call that *anger energy*. The following activities will teach you how to get rid of anger energy in a way that keeps you and others safe and out of trouble.

THE VEGETABLE JIVE

Moving actively can help you get rid of
your anger energy in a wise way.
The music helps you get your mind off your anger,
and your movements help you get rid of your anger energy.

THE VEGETABLE HUG

Hugging something soft is very comforting.
When you feel angry, hugging a pillow or stuffed animal
can help you calm down.

THE VEGETABLE PUNCH

Hitting someone or something will leave you hurting, too.
Hit something soft instead. Hitting a pillow will help
release your anger energy in a safe way.

THE VEGETABLE THROW

Imagine placing your angry feelings in the palm of your hand.
Make a tight fist. Now throw that angry feeling as far as you can.
This helps you get rid of your anger energy
without hurting yourself or anyone else.

STORYTELLING GUIDANCE © 2004 MAR✳CO PRODUCTS, INC. 1-800-448-2197

THE VEGETABLE TALK ROLE-PLAY SITUATION CARDS

Have each child select a partner. One child pretends to be angry. The other should be the listener. Using one of the situations listed below, have the child who is angry express how he/she feels. Then have the partners switch roles and role-play the situation again.

You got blamed for something you did not do.	Your sister is trying to pick a fight with you.	You are grounded for screaming at your mother.
You broke your favorite toy.	Your sister tattled on you.	It's raining and your baseball game has been cancelled.
You were pushed by a bigger kid.	Your dad won't buy you the new skateboard you've been wanting.	You are running late for school because you could not find your favorite shirt.
You lost your snack money.	Your best friend won't talk to you.	Your sister took your CD without your permission.
Your best friend made fun of you.	Your parents don't allow you to call your friends on the phone.	You forgot to bring your homework home from school.
Your mother yelled at you for not cleaning your room.	You can't stay up past 9:00, and you really feel you should.	Your pet has died.
You have lots of homework. So you won't be able to watch your favorite TV show.	A tire on your bike is flat.	A bully at school tries to bully you into giving him your spending money.

STORYTELLING GUIDANCE © 2004 MAR∗CO PRODUCTS, INC. 1-800-448-2197

SWIMMING WITH THE FISH

(Friendship and Character Education)

OBJECTIVE:

To teach children appropriate behaviors for making and keeping friends. Children will also analyze whether their own behaviors are appropriate ways to keep friends.

MATERIALS NEEDED:

For each child:
- ☐ Copy of *Swimming With The Fish* (pages 32-42)
- ☐ Copy of the fish patterns and *Swimming With The Friendly Fish* (pages 43-44)
- ☐ Copy of *Friends Are...* (page 45)
- ☐ Pencil
- ☐ Crayons or markers
- ☐ Scissors
- ☐ Paste or glue stick

For the leader:
- ☐ Stapler and staples

PRE-PRESENTATION PREPARATION:

Reproduce the necessary materials for the children. Staple the story pages together into a booklet for each child. Read the story. Be prepared to review any unfamiliar or difficult-to-read words with the children prior to distributing the booklets.

INTRODUCING THE LESSON:

Have the children sit in a circle. Then say:

> Today I am going to pretend to be one of your friends. I am going to say some words. I want you to tell me if what you hear would make you want me for a friend.

Then say the following three sentences, pausing after each one, for the children's comments:

> I don't like playing with you.
> You are no fun at all.
> You are a big crybaby.

Now I want you to listen to the words I am going to say. Then I want you to tell me if they would make you want me for a friend.

Say the next three sentences, pausing after each one for the children's comments:

> I have a new video game at home. Would you like to come over and try it out?
> That's a great new mitt you have! Sometime would you bring it and play catch with me?
> Do you really like these cupcakes? Would you like me to show you how I made them?

The things we say and do make the difference between having and not having friends. If we make nice comments to others and treat them kindly, we will have friends. But if we constantly say mean things or treat others in a cruel way, we might not have any friends at all.

Today we are going to read about two fish who are surrounded by several different kinds of fish. They want to choose their friends wisely. They want to hang out with fish who are kind and respectful. In order to do this, they need your help. They are going to introduce you to some fish they have just met. They would like you to help them decide if they should swim with these fish.

Introduce any unfamiliar or difficult-to-read words used in the story.

If the children are reading the story themselves or as a group, distribute *Swimming With The Fish,* crayons or markers, and a pencil to each child. Have the children take turns reading the story aloud. After reading each page and before going on to the next, have the children complete the activities on the page that's been read. You may briefly discuss their answers.

After reading the story, give each child the fish patterns, *Swimming With Friendly Fish,* scissors, and paste or a glue stick. Explain the activity by saying:

> Look at the fish on this page. Select those whose behaviors would make a good friend. Cut them out, then paste them in the water on the next page. When you have finished cutting and pasting the fish, color your picture. If you finish coloring your picture before everyone else is finished, you may color the other pictures in your book.

When everyone has completed the activity, have some of the children share their pictures with the group. Then distribute *Friends Are...* Review each word with the children, then have them follow the directions and circle those traits that friends possess. When all the students have completed the activity, display them in an area where they can remind the children about the type of behaviors that promote friendships.

Thank the children for their cooperation. Tell them they may take their storybooks and activity sheets home.

SWIMMING WITH THE FISH

Hi! My name is Kitty Catfish. This is my brother, Tom Catfish. We belong to a school of fish. In some ways we fish are all alike. In other ways, we are very different.

We meet all kinds of fish in our school every day. And we have to decide whether we would like to swim with these fish. Sometimes it's a little hard to decide. Maybe you can help us!

Let me introduce you to a few of the fish in our school.

Draw a picture of you and your brother or sister.
If you have do not have a brother or sister,
draw a picture of yourself.

This is Sam Shark. He is not very nice. He always says really mean things. He pushes us and calls us nasty names. When we swim next to him, we always end up feeling bad. Should we swim with Sam Shark?

Circle the fish that shows how you would feel if Sam Shark did these mean things to you.

If you knew someone like Sam Shark, would you be his or her friend?

YES   NO

STORYTELLING GUIDANCE © 2004 MAR✳CO PRODUCTS, INC. 1-800-448-2197

Find and color the hidden word in the picture that describes Dolores Dolphin.

Do you think Dolores Dolphin will make and keep friends?

YES   NO

HOW TO CATCH WORMS WITHOUT GETTING CAUGHT

CARING

This is Dolores Dolphin. Dolores is really smart.
She always helps others with their homework.
She always knows the right thing to do,
and she offers others good advice.
She cares about other fish.
Should we swim with Dolores Dolphin?

This is Spunky Salmon. Spunky is a lot of fun.
He is always excited about something.
He can always find something good about everyone and everything.
When we feel sad, Spunky cheers us up.
Should we swim with Spunky Salmon?

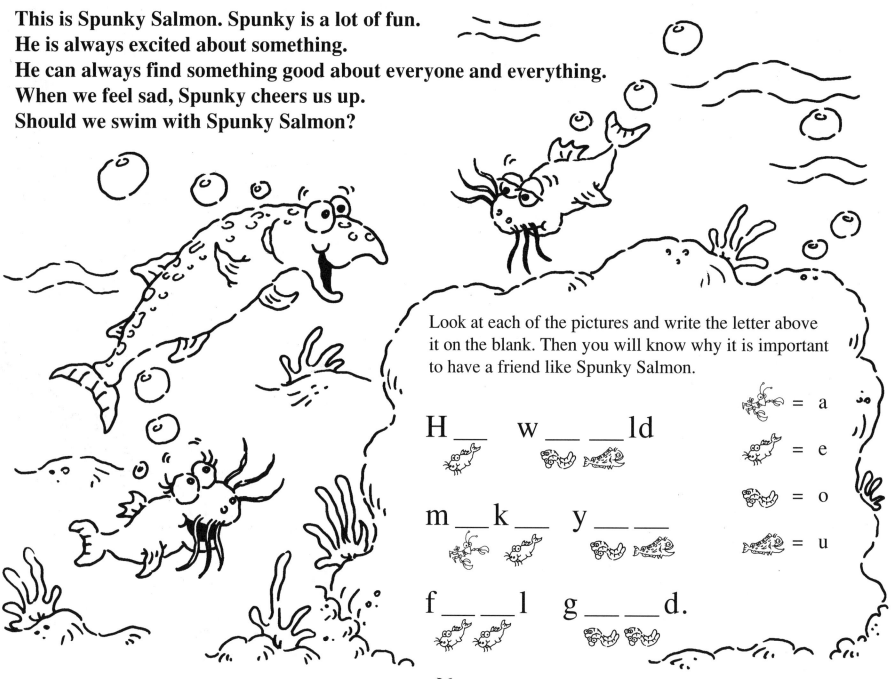

Look at each of the pictures and write the letter above it on the blank. Then you will know why it is important to have a friend like Spunky Salmon.

H__ w __ __ld

m__k__ y___

f___l g___d.

= a

= e

= o

= u

STORYTELLING GUIDANCE © 2004 MAR✷CO PRODUCTS, INC. 1-800-448-2197

Put an ✗ on the fish that shows how Trudy makes you feel.

This is Trudy Tuna. She is full of stories.
Sometimes she tells stories that we know are not true.
Sometimes she lies to her parents and teachers.
She lies to us all the time, too.
Should we swim with Trudy Tuna?

STORYTELLING GUIDANCE © 2004 MAR✶CO PRODUCTS, INC. 1-800-448-2197

This is Maria Mahi-Mahi. She is responsible, and she always tries to do the right thing. She never lies or steals. She turns her homework in on time. Maria treats everyone nicely and does everything her parents and teachers ask her to do. Should we swim with Maria Mahi-Mahi?

Fill in the missing letters.

Maria Mahi-Mahi is:

R __ __ P O __ S __ __ __ E

Put an ✘ on the face that shows how Maria Mahi-Mahi makes you feel.

This is Sally Swordfish. Sally loves to play all kinds of sports. She lets everyone play, even if they don't play very well. Sally is really nice. She does not get mad if her team loses a game. Should we swim with Sally Swordfish?

Circle the correct answer:

Sally Swordfish:

a. hurts the feelings of others.
   YES   NO

b. is a poor sport.
   YES   NO

c. loves to play all kinds of sports.
   YES   NO

d. would get mad if her team lost a game.
   YES   NO

Would you let a player who was not a good batter be on your baseball team?

   YES   NO

Who do you know who makes you laugh?

_____

This is Peter Pike. He is really funny.
He always says things to make others laugh.
He is so easygoing! We never see him upset.
Should we swim with Peter Pike?

This is Hal Halibut. Or as he is known in the fish world, Heated Hal. Hal gets angry all the time. If he loses a game or something goes wrong, he gets upset. It's okay to get upset, but Hal often throws things and breaks them or hits someone. Should we swim with Hal Halibut?

Draw a line from each statement that describes Hal Halibut to the picture of Hal Halibut.

Hal Halibut:

a. is a good sport.

b. gets angry all the time.

c. hits others when he is angry.

d. is fun to be around.

e. breaks things when he is angry.

This is Cindy Cod. Cindy takes things that don't belong to her. She steals candy from the candy store. She has even taken toys from us. Should we swim with Cindy Cod?

Circle the correct answer:

Swimming with Cindy Cod could:

get us in trouble.	YES	NO
make other fish think we are like her.	YES	NO
make us lose our other friends.	YES	NO

If Cindy wants more friends, she will have to:

keep doing what she is doing.	YES	NO
become trustworthy.	YES	NO
bully others into being her friends.	YES	NO

Cut out the fish who show behaviors that will make good friends.
Glue them on the following page, *Swimming With The Friendly Fish.*

SWIMMING WITH THE FRIENDLY FISH

FRIENDS ARE ...

Circle the following words that you believe describe a friend.

hits	brags	lies
yells	gives	truthful
smiles	nice	steals
cares	helpful	responsible
frowns	listens	fun
cries	mean	kind
whines	rude	angry
shares	positive	honest

STORYTELLING GUIDANCE © 2004 MAR*CO PRODUCTS, INC. 1-800-448-2197

TONI THE BULLY

(Handling A Bully)

OBJECTIVE:

Children will learn that bullies are unhappy and often have secret reasons for behaving the way they do. They will experience the results of positive and negative reactions to bullying behaviors.

MATERIALS NEEDED:

For each child:
- ☐ Copy of *Toni The Bully* (pages 48-53)
- ☐ Copy of *How To Stop A Bully* (page 54)
- ☐ Pencil

For each student group:
- ☐ *Dealing With Bully Behaviors* gameboard (page 55)
- ☐ *Dealing With Bully Behaviors* cards (pages 56-57)
- ☐ Die
- ☐ Game pieces for each child in the group

For the leader:
- ☐ Stapler and staples
- ☐ Scissors
- ☐ Rubberbands
- ☐ 2 small animal puppets
- ☐ Chalkboard and chalk

PRE-PRESENTATION PREPARATION:

Reproduce the necessary materials for the children. Staple the story pages together into a booklet for each child. Read the story. Be prepared to review any unfamiliar or difficult-to-read words with the children prior to distributing the booklets. Reproduce a gameboard and set of cards for each student group. Cut the cards apart. Secure each set of cards with a rubberband.

INTRODUCING THE LESSON:

Introduce the lesson by using the puppets to illustrate bullying. Have one puppet threaten the other into doing something like giving him a dollar. Continue the puppet interaction through several verbal exchanges. Then ask:

What is a bully? *(A bully is someone who gets others to do things by scaring them with threats.)*

What do you think it might be like to be bullied? *(Accept any appropriate answers.)*

Then say:

Today we are going to learn why some bullies behave the way they do and how we can help them change the way they behave.

Introduce any unfamiliar or difficult-to-read words used in the story.

If the children are reading the story themselves or as a group, distribute *Toni The Bully* and a pencil to each child. Have the children take turns reading the story aloud. After reading each page and before going on to the next, have the children complete the activities on the page that's been read. You may briefly discuss their answers.

After reading the story, say:

In our story, we learned about a dog who was a bully. He threatened and punished the other dogs. Is this the same as or different from a boy or girl who is a bully? *(It is the same. Boys and girls who are bullies would also threaten or punish others.)*

What are some ways bullies might threaten or punish kids your age? *(Accept all appropriate answers and write them on the chalkboard.)*

Distribute *How To Stop A Bully* to each child. Review each point. Then have the children role-play each situation written on the chalkboard. Tell them to use the techniques on their information sheet.

Divide the children into groups of three or four. Give each group a die, game pieces for each child, a *Dealing With Bully Behaviors* gameboard, and a set of *Dealing With Bully Behaviors* cards. Have the children place their game pieces on "Start." Then say:

The oldest child in each group will start, then the next oldest will take a turn and so on until everyone has had a turn. Continue in this order throughout the game. When it is your turn, throw the die and move your game piece the number of spaces that you rolled. You must follow the directions on the space where you have landed. If you land on a space with a picture of Toni, wait there until your next turn. If you land on a *Pick A Card* space and need help reading the card, raise your hand. I will help you. Continue the game until I say time is up.

When the allotted time has elapsed, collect the gameboards and cards. Ask several children to tell the group what they learned from the game.

Thank the children for their cooperation. Tell them they may take their storybooks and posters home and color them.

STORYTELLING GUIDANCE © 2004 MAR*CO PRODUCTS, INC. 1-800-448-2197

TONI THE BULLY

Toni was a dog who was really, really mean. She loved to pick on others and beat them up. In order to get other dogs to do things with her, she would threaten to bite them or punish them by locking them in a doghouse. She thought threats and punishments would force them to be her friends. But she really didn't have any friends. She was a bully.

Draw a line from the words that tell why Toni was a bully to the picture of Toni.

Toni was a bully because she:

threatened to hurt the other dogs.

ignored the other dogs and played by herself.

liked picking on the other dogs and hurting them.

shared her toys with others.

STORYTELLING GUIDANCE © 2004 MAR✳CO PRODUCTS, INC. 1-800-448-2197

What the other dogs didn't know was that Toni was really, really sad. Her master had treated her very badly. She was hit and yelled at all the time. Many times she was even locked in her doghouse and not given any dinner. One day, Toni's master decided he did not want her any more. He took her to the dog pound.

Circle the faces that show how Toni felt about her master.

One day, a nice family came to the pound. They saw Toni and thought she would be a nice dog for their family. What they did not know was that Toni wasn't happy. She was angry deep inside. Even though she was no longer being hit, yelled at, or starved, Toni could not forget the lessons she had learned from her other master. So when she went out into her new neighborhood, she behaved badly all the time.

Draw Toni's face showing how she felt inside.

Do you think boys and girls who are bullies feel the same way?

YES   NO

No one could understand Toni's behavior. She lived with a nice family. She was treated well. The dogs were very confused. One day Penny the Poodle, who lived down the street, told the other dogs that maybe there was something none of them knew about Toni. Penny said that maybe something the others dogs didn't know about made Toni act the way she did.

Do you think Penny's reason for Toni's behavior is correct?

YES   NO

STORYTELLING GUIDANCE © 2004 MAR✳CO PRODUCTS, INC. 1-800-448-2197

After listening to Penny, the dogs decided they would try something new. They would not get scared or run and hide when Toni came near them.

When Toni threatened them, they would talk nicely to her. They would tell her nicely why they would not do what she wanted. They would suggest that she play with them. They would show her how to be a friend.

52

Look at each of the pictures. Write the letter on the blank above it.
Then you will know how the animals taught Toni to stop being a bully.

Th__ y   sh __ w __ __

h __ r   h __ w   t __

b __   a   f r __ __ n __.

= d

= e

= i

= o

HOW TO STOP A BULLY

When someone bullies you:

1. **Look directly into the bully's eyes.
    Then speak.**

2. **Tell the bully, "Stop it."**
    "Stop threatening to take my lunch money."

3. **Then tell the bully how his/her behavior is making you feel.**
    *"Every time you do this, I feel sad because you don't have enough money.
    And I feel angry that you don't want me to eat lunch."*

4. **Finally, offer another suggestion.**
    *"Maybe you could ask your parents for more money.
    Or you could tell the teacher that you don't have enough money for lunch.
    She could see about getting you on the Free Lunch Program."*

STORYTELLING GUIDANCE © 2004 MAR✳CO PRODUCTS, INC. 1-800-448-2197

DEALING WITH BULLY BEHAVIORS GAMEBOARD

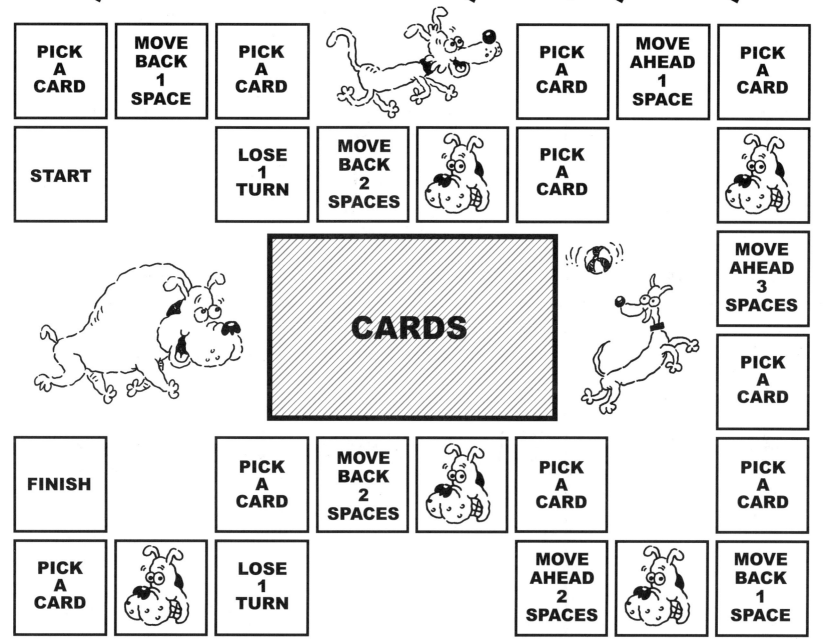

You were nice to a bully.
Move ahead 1 space.

You smiled at a bully.
Move ahead 2 spaces.

You invited a bully
to play with you.
Move ahead 2 spaces.

You helped someone
stand up to a bully.
Move ahead 2 spaces.

You stopped a bully
from hurting someone.
Move ahead 2 spaces.

You bullied a younger child
into giving you some money.
Move back 2 spaces.

You shared your snack
with a bully.
Move ahead 1 space.

You said, "Good Morning"
to a bully.
Move ahead 1 space.

You bullied your friend into
giving you her video game.
Move back 2 spaces.

You understand why bullies
behave the way they do.
You want to help them.
Move ahead 1 space.

You gave a bully
a compliment
Move ahead 2 spaces.

You bullied someone into
buying you some ice cream.
Move back 1 space.

You are not a bully.
Move ahead 2 spaces.

DEALING WITH BULLY BEHAVIORS CARDS
STORYTELLING GUIDANCE © 2004 MAR-CO PRODUCTS, INC.

You told the teacher
about someone bullying you.
Move ahead 1 space.

DEALING WITH BULLY BEHAVIORS CARDS
STORYTELLING GUIDANCE © 2004 MAR-CO PRODUCTS, INC.

You lied to the teacher
to protect a bully.
Move back 1 space.

DEALING WITH BULLY BEHAVIORS CARDS
STORYTELLING GUIDANCE © 2004 MAR-CO PRODUCTS, INC.

You like to watch bullies
pick on others.
Move back 2 spaces.

DEALING WITH BULLY BEHAVIORS CARDS
STORYTELLING GUIDANCE © 2004 MAR-CO PRODUCTS, INC.

You gave the bully
what she wanted.
Move back 1 space.

DEALING WITH BULLY BEHAVIORS CARDS
STORYTELLING GUIDANCE © 2004 MAR-CO PRODUCTS, INC.

You helped a bully get up
after he fell down.
Move ahead 1 space.

DEALING WITH BULLY BEHAVIORS CARDS
STORYTELLING GUIDANCE © 2004 MAR-CO PRODUCTS, INC.

You laugh when
someone is bullied.
Move back to the nearest
"Pick A Card" space.

DEALING WITH BULLY BEHAVIORS CARDS
STORYTELLING GUIDANCE © 2004 MAR-CO PRODUCTS, INC.

You told a bully you would
not give her your candy bar.
You said you would
share it with her.
Move ahead 1 space.

DEALING WITH BULLY BEHAVIORS CARDS
STORYTELLING GUIDANCE © 2004 MAR-CO PRODUCTS, INC.

You act like a bully with your
younger sister and brother.
Go back to the nearest
"Pick A Card" space.

DEALING WITH BULLY BEHAVIORS CARDS
STORYTELLING GUIDANCE © 2004 MAR-CO PRODUCTS, INC.

You looked a bully right
in the eye and said, "no."
Move ahead 2 spaces.

DEALING WITH BULLY BEHAVIORS CARDS
STORYTELLING GUIDANCE © 2004 MAR-CO PRODUCTS, INC.

You watched someone
get bullied.
You did not do
anything about it.
Move back 3 spaces.

DEALING WITH BULLY BEHAVIORS CARDS
STORYTELLING GUIDANCE © 2004 MAR-CO PRODUCTS, INC.

You bully your cousin
when he comes to visit.
Move back 1 space.

DEALING WITH BULLY BEHAVIORS CARDS
STORYTELLING GUIDANCE © 2004 MAR-CO PRODUCTS, INC.

MISS WINGATE'S EARS ARE GROWING

(Tattling)

OBJECTIVE:

Children will learn the difference between tattling and reporting. Children will learn to report only when someone is in trouble or in danger or when property is being damaged.

MATERIALS NEEDED:

For each child:
- ☐ Copy of *Miss Wingate's Ears Are Growing* (pages 60-69)
- ☐ Copy of *Reporting Rules* (page 70)
- ☐ Copy of *Reporting Or Tattling?* (page 71)
- ☐ Pencil
- ☐ Crayons or markers (include a red crayon and green crayon)

For the leader:
- ☐ Stapler and staples

PRE-PRESENTATION PREPARATION:

Reproduce the necessary materials for the children. Staple the story pages together into a booklet for each child. Read the story. Be prepared to review any unfamiliar or difficult-to-read words with the children prior to distributing the booklets.

INTRODUCING THE LESSON:

In the story we are going to read today, you will hear a little rhyme that goes like this:

Tattle, tattle, that's all I ever hear.
Please stop, boys and girls. It's hurting my ears.

What do you think this means? *(Accept any appropriate answers.)*

Then tell the children:

Tattling is something that is done very often at school and at home. Do you know what tattling is? *(Pause for answers.)* Tattling is when someone tells on someone for doing something that is not hurting anyone or anything. For example, if you see someone stick his tongue out at you, is there a reason for you to tell the teacher? *(Pause for children to answer that you don't need to tell the teacher because the action is not hurting anyone.)* This is a situation you should try to handle yourself. You can tell the person to stop what he is doing. You can tell the person how what he is doing makes you feel.

Many times, children don't try to handle situations themselves. They call for the teacher's help right away. It's important to remember that there is only one teacher for all the students in your class. When you call for help you don't really need, you are taking away from the teacher's time. That's not fair to the other children.

Today you are going to learn about a class whose students always tattled. You are also going to learn what happened to the teacher of that class. You will learn how she had to teach the students when they should handle situations by themselves and when they should look for help.

Introduce any unfamiliar or difficult-to-read words used in the story.

If the children are reading the story themselves or as a group, distribute *Miss Wingate's Ears Are Growing,* crayons or markers, and a pencil to each child. Have the children take turns reading the story aloud. After reading each page and before going on to the next, have the children complete the activities on the page that's been read. You may briefly discuss their answers.

After reading the story, give each child *Rules For Reporting* and *Reporting Or Tattling?* Begin by reviewing the *Rules For Reporting.* Have the children give examples of each rule.

Tell the children to take out a red and green crayon. Instruct them to read each situation on *Tattling Or Reporting?* Tell them to circle the tattling situations in red and the reporting situations in green. Tell the students how much time they have to complete the activity. Tell those who finish the activity sheet before the allotted time is up that they may begin coloring the illustrations in their book.

When the allotted time has elapsed, have the children correct their own papers. Say:

I will read each situation. If you have it circled in green, stand up. If you have it circled in red, sit down or stay seated.

Review the situations on the activity sheet. Thank the children for their attention and participation. Tell them to take their books, posters, and activity sheets home. Encourage them to read their storybook with their parents.

STORYTELLING GUIDANCE © 2004 MAR✶CO PRODUCTS, INC. 1-800-448-2197

MISS WINGATE'S EARS ARE GROWING

Miss Wingate is a first-grade teacher at Forest Hills Elementary School. She loves her job. She would look forward to going to school each day except for one thing. She always hears her children say the same kind of thing over and over.

STORYTELLING GUIDANCE © 2004 MAR✲CO PRODUCTS, INC. 1-800-448-2197

"Miss Wingate, Randy Raccoon pulled my hair."
"Miss Wingate, Suzie Skunk hit me."
"Miss Wingate, Billy Beaver won't share."

"Tattle, tattle, that's all I ever hear.
Please stop, boys and girls. It's hurting my ears."

Find and color the hidden word in the picture that tells what the problem was in Miss Wingate's class.

Circle the picture that shows how big Miss Wingate's ears are now.

Each time the animals tattled,
Miss Wingate hummed this little tune.
Then she felt a tingle in her ears.
Miss Wingate's ears were growing just
a little every time someone tattled.

STORYTELLING GUIDANCE © 2004 MAR✳CO PRODUCTS, INC. 1-800-448-2197

Day after day, the children kept tattling.

"Miss Wingate Mark Mole isn't sitting correctly."
"Miss Wingate, Dora Deer is picking her nose."
"Miss Wingate, Rachel Rabbit is combing her hair."

Miss Wingate was so tired of tattling! She hummed to herself.

"Tattle, tattle, that's all I ever hear. Please stop, boys and girls. It's hurting my ears."

Miss Wingate felt more tingling in her ears. Her ears had grown slightly bigger that day.

Circle the correct answer:

You should tell the teacher if someone:

a. isn't sitting correctly in his chair.   YES   NO

b. is combing her hair.   YES   NO

c. is hitting you.   YES   NO

Circle the picture that shows how big Miss Wingate's ears are now.

Miss Wingate begged the boys and girls to stop. But the children kept tattling until Miss Wingate's ears were really, really big. "Tattle, tattle, that's all I ever hear. Please stop, boys and girls. It's hurting my ears," she hummed.

Oscar Owl noticed Miss Wingate's
ears and began to scream.
"Look at Miss Wingate's ears.
They're really, really big.
Our tattling has made her ears really ring.
Each time they get bigger and bigger.
Please, Miss Wingate, teach us to stop tattling.
We don't like your big ears."

Cross out the picture that
shows how Miss Wingate felt.

Circle the picture that shows how
big Miss Wingate's ears are now.

"Okay." said Miss Wingate.
She asked the boys and girls to sit on the floor.
They listened carefully as she began to explain.

"Tell if someone is hurt or in trouble.
Tell if property is being damaged.
Don't bother with the little things
that no one has the time to manage."

The boys and girls nodded their heads as
they listened to Miss Wingate's rhyme.
They told her they were willing to try.

Circle the pictures that show times when you should tell an adult.

STORYTELLING GUIDANCE © 2004 MAR✳CO PRODUCTS, INC. 1-800-448-2197

Wanda Wolf saw Peter Puma drop a paper on the floor. She didn't say a word.

Miss Wingate's ears got a little smaller.

STORYTELLING GUIDANCE © 2004 MAR✶CO PRODUCTS, INC. 1-800-448-2197

Sammy Snake saw Betty Bear make a face at Mindy Mouse. He kept that to himself.

Miss Wingate's ears got a little smaller.

Cross out the picture of Betty Bear's face that shows how she felt when Sammy Snake did not tattle on her.

Circle the picture that shows how big Miss Wingate's ears are now.

STORYTELLING GUIDANCE © 2004 MAR✳CO PRODUCTS, INC. 1-800-448-2197

It took three days for Miss Wingate's ears to return to their normal size. The students became nicer, and now Miss Wingate hums a new song.

"Thank you for reporting when someone is in trouble. Thank you for reporting when property's being damaged. Please keep on reporting when you see a problem happening. It will help me ever so much to bad behavior manage."

Circle the picture that shows how big Miss Wingate's ears are now.

Draw how you think Miss Wingate feels now.

STORYTELLING GUIDANCE © 2004 MAR∗CO PRODUCTS, INC. 1-800-448-2197

REPORTING RULES

~1~
Tell if
someone is hurt.

~2~
Tell if someone
is in trouble.

~3~
Tell if property
is being damaged.

REPORTING OR TATTLING?

Circle in green the situations that are reporting and that you would definitely tell the teacher about.
Circle in red the situations that are tattling.

Someone is running in the hall.

Someone is beating up someone else.

Someone stuck his tongue out at you.

Someone is hitting your friend on the head.

Someone is writing on the bathroom wall.

Someone just spilled her milk.

Someone spit on the floor.

Someone is writing on the bathroom wall.

Someone is breaking schoolroom windows.

Someone is tearing up a library book.

Someone is pulling someone else's hair.

Someone is kicking your friend really hard.

Someone just tapped you on the shoulder.

Someone is throwing paper on the floor.

Someone is calling you names.

Someone is talking when she should be quiet.

Someone did not say, "Hi" to you today.

Someone is making a face at you.

STORYTELLING GUIDANCE © 2004 MAR✳CO PRODUCTS, INC. 1-800-448-2197

MELINDA SAENZ VILLEGAS

Storytelling has been part of my life as long as I can remember. It began when, as an adolescent, I heard my twin sister tell an amazing story to two of my nieces. It was a story that dealt with self-esteem and accepting differences. It was a story unlike any I had ever heard, and motivated me to begin making up stories of my own.

That experience of sharing tales with my nieces still lingers dear in my heart. And every story I write somehow reminds me of the one my sister told. As an educator and counselor for 18 years, I have always used storytelling to help children learn new concepts or skills. Some may say that I make life more difficult for myself because I would rather make up a story than open a book and simply read one. But I say I make my life more interesting that way.